THERE ARE LADIES PRESENT

"Approach, women of Athens!"

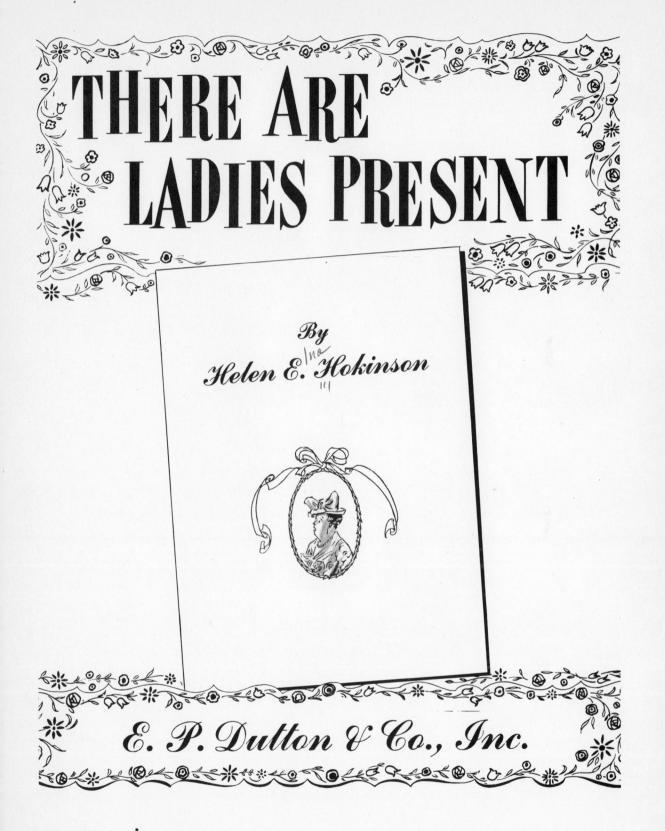

THERE ARE LADIES PRESENT

By
Helen E. Hokinson

E. P. Dutton & Co., Inc.

E·P·DUTTON & CO. INC.
1852 1952
CELEBRATING 100 YEARS OF PUBLISHING

THERE ARE LADIES PRESENT

"It has to be large enough
for two birds who are in love with each other."

6

"I want you to give me your solemn promise not to bolt
the Republican Party without having a heart-to-heart talk with me first."

"*By the way, when we talk to my husband about Westport, maybe we'd better just not mention the artists.*"

"It is unfortunate that our treasurer moved to another town without <u>explaining</u> anything."

"I always mistrust them when they take a lot of prizes."

"Is it true that the White Mountains have been going downhill?"

"*But isn't there some sort of __mock__ gin?*"

"I forgot the exact address, but you'll know the house because the first-floor drapes are dark blue with little white chrysanthemums."

"Well, if I were President of the United States, I wouldn't give jobs to everybody I play cards with."

PAPER SALVAGE

"I thought a few flowers would brighten up the place."

"Well, this man and this woman go off into the woods to live
with nothing but the clothes on their backs. It's awfully
interesting, but you'll be exhausted."

"Have you driven the new Buick with wizard control?"

"*But Madam President, I think we should all take*
<u>turns</u> at entertaining people <u>like</u> Thornton Wilder."

"How is your sense of humor today, Mrs. Ridgely?"

"And now, shall we make one little concession to winter?"

*"I'm going to send you the most **wonderful Swede** for your arthritis."*

"You can see my problem—there's no mystery."

*"Did you ever happen to hear of such
a thing as 'Glamour?'"*

"Would the Fifty-ninth Street Longchamps be crowded?"

"He wants to whisper something."

*"We used to know some people who **had** a formal garden, but they drank."*

"There **isn't** much I can
do. This one eyebrow is naturally quizzical."

"I'm afraid I bit off more 'Robert E. Lee' than I could chew."

"I know you're all as sorry as I am
that the Chinese shadow plays last Saturday failed to bring out the husbands."

"Do you suppose I really could jolly my husband into the Black Hills?"

"If I weren't a guest of this club, I'd have some very severe words to say about pruning laurel."

*"Heavens! Who is that **tall man** standing beside Harriet?"*

"Just say, 'Entertained a few members of the younger married set at bridge.'"

"Ahem. Oh, Cummings!"

"Now, before I send you to this houseparty in Southampton, perhaps
I ought to tell you a few things."

"I haven't any use for
a detective who lets five or six people get killed."

"If it gives Madame a stomach we can take it out."

"Are we __very__ far from civilization?"

"Any liquor, narcotics, tobacco, firearms, or explosives?"

"There's twelve cents due on John Marquand."

"I believe we're next door. Aren't you the apartment with dinner chimes?"

"Of course some cats have eight kittens but I never have more than six."

29

"I loved it where she said she'd never give him up—never, never, never!"

"You ought to come to Palm Beach. I have the cleverest
little nose-and-throat man there."

"A baby right here on Fifth Avenue! Isn't this an amazing city!"

"Suppose you was called upon to defend a woman's honor."

*"Which is the play
that we read deserves
the whole town's immediate and rapt attention?"*

33

"When I was a girl I
was so crazy about Napoleon
my father was worried."

"I'm hungry. What about you?"

"It has been moved that our recording secretary send a summary of today's discussion to Marshal Tito. Do I hear a second?"

"We raised it from one of the canary's
seeds. We'd always wondered what they were like."

"What a pity Mrs. Thompson is the way she is."

"Did you know that the stock-market page has a very clever column that tells everybody exactly what to invest *in*?"

"What I really wanted was something for an <u>older</u> dog."

"Perhaps I ought to explain that we're beginning to think about boys."

"But I thought people only went to Wisconsin on business."

"It's my birthday, and my husband said to get the works."

"Don't forget I want to come back by way of my sister-in-law."

"The room clerk <u>assured</u> me that all the animals here will run away from me."

"It gives me great pleasure to announce that the rummage sale will definitely result in John Charles Thomas."

"How does your skin react to secret ingredients?"

"Has our convoy to Mt. Vernon gone by here?"

"His mother came from the *Bide-A-Wee* Home, but only a few friends of the family know it."

"It won't start multiplying before I get it to my little nephew, will it?"

*"Life says that it will send a photographer to our cake sale
if it possibly can."*

"... *music, dramatics, careful health supervision, organized play, a thirteen-acre campus studded with fine old maples. Character and individuality are stressed ...*"

"*Can't you put down that detective story for even a minute, George? You're supposed to be on a vacation.*"

"I want everything!"

"I want a hat. *Just a plain, ordinary hat.*"

"In short, the Civic Betterment League would like to see a nice high hedge around your place."

"I don't believe it's generally known that Mrs.
Birtwell has had a poem accepted by 'Driftwind.'"

"You *know* it's beautiful—you just won't admit it."

"Henry! Are you listening or are you just thinking?"

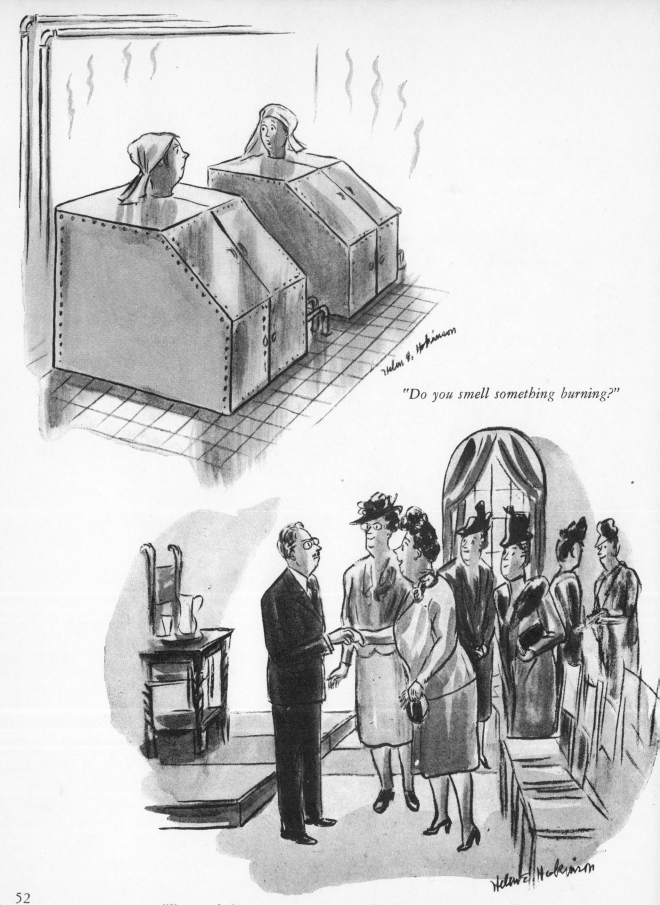

"Do you smell something burning?"

"I'm so glad to meet you, Mr. Hutchins. I want to tell you how
much I enjoyed wading through your last book."

"I want you to meet a charming vote I've rounded up for you."

"Why, I'd <u>love</u> an Armenian! Are they any good?"

53

"What do you think—should I plunge
right into all the Iron Curtain countries or just take up Czechoslovakia?"

"Then she told Gary Cooper she could
never love him, and Gary Cooper winced."

"Is that clock right?"

"I tell you what you could do. You
could load yourself down with costume jewelry."

55

*"Our straw vote has resulted in
nineteen votes for the Republicans and one for the Democrats."*

"How perfectly uncanny! My Greek is coming back to me."

"Let's see—
they make something
here, don't they?"

"Edmund, are you a bull or a bear? You've
never told me."

"Now, don't make me meet _everyone_ in Southampton!"

"George, I have a confession to make. We
own a thousand _bushels_ of September wheat."

"Would it surprise you to hear that I composed a club song at Mt. Desert?"

*"Jack and I are going all over <u>creation</u> this summer—if
we can sublet our apartment."*

59

"I'd never let a doll of mine wear a dress like that."

"I suppose you develop a sixth sense, or something."

"I visited Byron's and Shelley's tombs, and _boy,_ are they neglected!"

"Shouldn't he have caught that?"

*"And the Swami says if everyone only
breathed properly, we wouldn't have all these wars."*

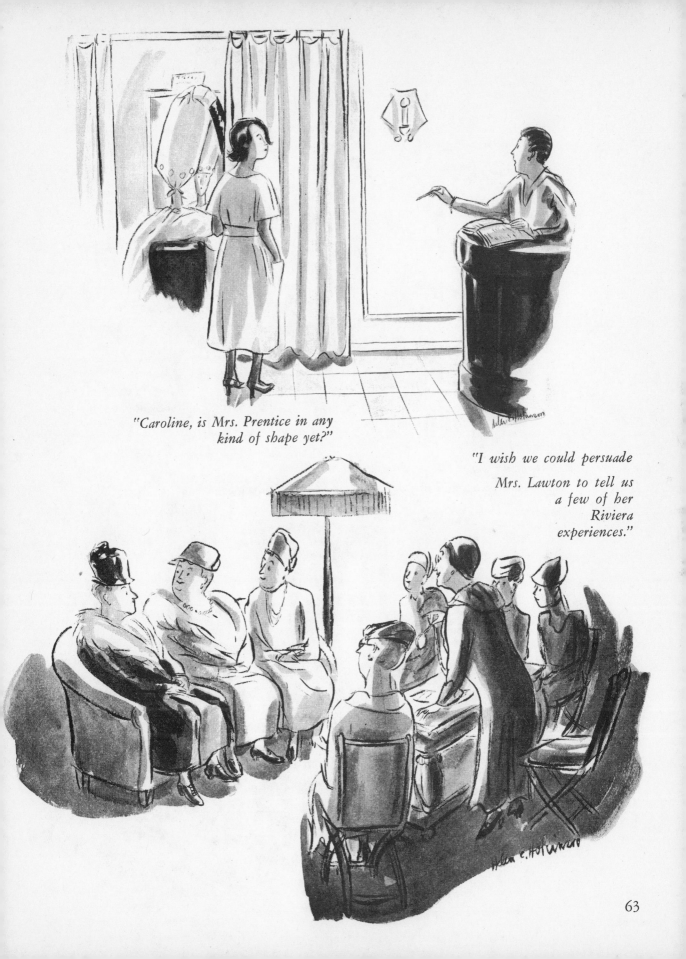

"Caroline, is Mrs. Prentice in any
kind of shape yet?"

"I wish we could persuade
Mrs. Lawton to tell us
a few of her
Riviera
experiences."

"*Well, I would never allow myself to become infatuated with royalty!*"

64

"*And you really want me to be Lady Macbeth?*"

"The treasurer wishes me to report that she has a sick headache."

*"Oh, Mr. Russell, is it all right for eight women
to come in here alone?"*

Waiting to be told that whatever they want is not to be found.

A reading-room siren

LIBRARY
FAUNA

One o'clock

SCHOOL
DAYS

"You know perfectly well, Louise, that six and four are not eleven."

"Is life so sweet, comma, or peace so dear, comma . . . ?"

An advanced student

"I thought you said there weren't any fascinating men left in Oyster Bay."

"We come here every summer. George was born
on a farm, you know."

"Would anyone like to argue with Mrs. Allen about the Truman Doctrine?"

"This is the one the guidebook says is so homelike, Momma."

"Since you're out there, young man, will you please give those poor little birds their luncheon?"

"Of course, we don't very often hear of an elopement in our set."

"Some day I'm going to sit down and
really learn to play cards."

"It isn't that there aren't plenty of men in Vermont, it's
just that you have to _look_ for them."

"Now when
we go in you
mustn't say,
'Hello, Mrs.
Bartlett.
Hello, Mr.
Bartlett.'
You must
say 'How
do you do?'"
"Yes, mother, and I
won't say 'often'—I'll say 'frequently.'"

"*What happened to Waverly Place?*"

"Why, I'm Sadie Thompson—you know, that girl in a play."

"I've come to get my Easter face."

"*Buon giorno, Scuola Berlitz. Il Signor Esposito, per favore.*"

"There must be something in Tiffany's a young ensign could use on a minesweeper."

"*Please tell Mrs. Anderson to cast on forty
Germantown. Then join French Zephyr. First two
rows, knit one, purl one, with Germantown; second two, knit one, purl one, with
Zephyr. Then repeat. I'm sure she'll have no trouble.*"

"Oh, I forgot to tell you. Come as _pirates_."

"Then how _do_ you intend to get to house furnishings?"

*"The question is, do we want to fall
back on Gilbert and Sullivan or do we want to fall back on Ibsen?"*

"Hasn't Silvermine just <u>gobs</u> of atmosphere!"